THE GRATEFUL DAD'S
JOURNAL OF
GRATITUDE

*A Daily Place to
Celebrate Your Life*

*Doug Gertner, Ph.D.
The Grateful Dad®*

Published by

 **press**

Hatching New Ideas Daily
Denver, Colorado

We plant fifteen seedling trees for every 300 Gratitude Journals printed — thanks to www.ReplantTrees.org

ISBN 978-0-9910743-0-3

For more information about how to bring on
The Grateful Dad, contact:
Doug Gertner, Ph.D. / The Grateful Dad
7949 East 28th Place, Denver, CO 80238
303.377.8081 · 303.886.4114
doug@thegratefuldad.org · www.thegratefuldad.org

Table of Contents

Why Use a Gratitude Journal?

Gratitude is groovy! And gratitude is good for you. "Gratitude is literally one of the few things that can measurably change people's lives," writes psychologist Richard Emmons in his book, *Thanks! How the New Science of Gratitude Can Make You Happier.* Studies show that people who take time to record their reasons for giving thanks — rather than dwelling on negatives — also feel more loving, forgiving, joyful, enthusiastic and optimistic about their futures, while their family and friends report that they seem happier and are more pleasant to be around. Simply making time to be grateful each day benefits us in so many ways. That's why I recommend that everyone pick up a gratitude journal.

Hoping for more happiness? Try being more grateful. Need to get healthier? You definitely need a daily dose of gratitude. Want more money, friends, time, or just a greater sense of joy, contentment, and confidence? Who doesn't? And for anyone seeking more of the good stuff, it's a fact that more gratitude can bring it on.

That's my story. I call it "My Year of Living Gratefully." Coming off a prolonged period of difficulty, I was disconnected from myself, and other important people in my life. Uncertain of what I had and what I wanted, I was feeling lousy, my business was slow, and I saw mostly just the negative in most every situation. I knew something needed to change, and I credit The Grateful Dad with showing me the path out of this funk.

Since becoming a father I have celebrated the many joys that brings. As a longtime fan of the band the Grateful Dead, it was a natural for me to adopt the moniker and persona of The Grateful Dad. And in an effort to 'walk my talk,' I began the new year with a new gratitude journal, and made the commitment to be grateful every day, and note what it was I was thankful for. On my weekly web-radio show, in my blogs and speeches, I also recounted my gratitude and reflected on full-circle fatherhood. And it didn't take long before I saw benefits in every aspect of my life and work. It broke down a lot like this:

- **Confidence & Motivation** —The first steps toward feeling better about myself, and more ready to take on the world, were aided by support from friends, loved ones and great coaches. Surround yourself with folks who make you feel good and give good advice. Their advice will surely include keeping a gratitude journal.

- **Recognition & Opportunity** — Once my confidence rose, and with it my motivation, I became more focused, put gratitude front and center, and just put it out there into the world. Soon I was being invited to give talks, getting quoted in articles, and generally attracting positive people and great reactions to whatever I did. The more grateful I was, the more doors that opened for me.

- **Satisfaction & Productivity** — As my year of living gratefully continued, and each day I noted my gratitude for both the mundane and the profound, the one-time and the ongoing things going right in my life, I not only became more satisfied on a daily basis, but also more productive. Realizing how much I have going for me helped me get more done and so more of it.

- **Success & More Money** — Here's the crazy thing: during that entire year focused on gratitude, I actually worked less and made more money. It's true. I took off every Monday for my radio show which is unpaid, and had my highest annual income ever. Along with that, the listenership to my show climbed 15% each quarter of the year. Go figure? All I can point to is my investment in gratitude.

- **Joy & Contentment** — This is the most important and delightful reward from my year of living gratefully. Better than being recognized, or productive, or earning more, it's the sense of happiness and inner peace that is truly the best outcome of all. I need only recall how low I'd sunk, and that the path back up was paved with gratitude, and you can see why I am encouraging you to have a grateful day, every day.

Are you ready to give it a try?

At times our own light goes out and is rekindled by a spark from another person. Each of us has cause to think with deep gratitude of those who have lighted the flame within us.
— Albert Schweitzer

How to Use This Gratitude Journal

There's no one right way to do it. You just need to dive in and make it a practice to be aware and grateful every day. I began by heeding the suggestion of Sarah Ban Breathnach to note five things a day. That worked well and really helped me to focus on the many, varied aspects of my life to give thanks for. The people, the places, the privileges, the big ideas and the small gifts, all found a place on the pages of my gratitude journal. And the good stuff followed.

I recommend that you read on; there are some items here to give you inspiration and guidance. And when you get to the first journal page, just begin by recording what you feel grateful for in the moment. And keep doing it every day. The rewards multiply with the investment you make. A few more thoughts to guide you:

How: Begin by noting today's date in the blank at the top of the page.

When: Some folks like to end their day by journaling, to reflect back on the day's events and give thanks for them. Others suggest beginning the day by noting how much we have to be grateful for, and what we seek as we look forward. I say try both. You may find, as I have, that any time of day is a good time to write in a gratitude journal.

Where & What: A few facts about the day, including what's going on, where you are, and how you're feeling can fill the top part of the page.

What else: Try to note 3-5 things every day for which you feel grateful. Sometimes it helps to look for a wide range of different things to give thanks for. Stretch it and see what happens when you make it a point to see how many different and diverse areas you can identify for your gratitude. Or go the other way; it never hurts to repeat something. If you feel gratitude daily for some aspect of your life — health, a loved one, or the simple appreciation for running water — let these show up on a regular basis in your gratitude journal. And if it's tough to be grateful some days, just note one thing and put your journal aside until tomorrow.

To* versus *For: Think in terms of what you are grateful for, and whom you are grateful to. What do you have and experience, and who has provided you with what you have? Whether you start your entry with "I am so grateful to…" or "I am so grateful for…" your daily practice is right on track.

Give yourself a break: I know first-hand the benefits of daily gratitude journaling. I also know a lot about stress. Please, do not let this practice become stressful for you. The rewards of capturing what we are grateful for can be offset and overridden if they come with a sense of obligation and pressure. Sometime during the summer of my year of living gratefully, I gave myself a break and cut back from five to three things a day. And some days I didn't journal at all — but I did go back and reflect and try to add what I remembered being grateful for that day. With later journals I decided to just skip a day now and then; any time I get to journal is better than a day I don't.

A Four Worlds Gratitude Blessing

(Based on the Jewish mystical tradition of Kabbalah, and the belief that we live in four worlds simultaneously.)

I am aware and grateful for the four worlds in which I live…

I am grateful for the physical world, for the ground on which I walk, for the clean fresh air I breathe, the water pure and cold that flows over this planet. I am grateful for my body, and the life that runs through it, for every organ and limb, and for my physical health and the strength to arise and face each day, knowing that this is temporary, and that I must honor my body to keep it healthy. I am grateful for my beating heart, for my mobility, and for the ability to take in nourishment and expel waste, with gratitude for all of the basic building blocks of the physical world.

I am grateful for my emotional world, the ability to feel and sense. I am grateful for the feelings of joy, and also of sadness, and the range of emotions that I share with other humans. And because I feel, I am grateful for my ability to empathize with others, to know and understand their emotions, as I too have felt that way before, with gratitude in the world of emotions.

I am grateful for the mental or intellectual world of my thoughts and awareness, the world of knowing. I am grateful for the head on my shoulders that knows, and sees, and thinks, and I am most grateful when those thoughts are positive, and that I can learn something new from everyone I meet, and everything I read and encounter. I am grateful to be able to think and read and reason and speak and reflect and dream and debate and connect, with gratitude in this world of the mind.

And I am grateful for the spiritual world, the world of mystery and faith, the world I know without knowing, trust without seeing, and believe in without thinking. I am filled with gratitude and wonder for divine beauty, and for those many, many things I cannot explain that make up the spiritual world for which I feel eternal gratitude.

For these four worlds — the physical, emotional, mental, and spiritual — in which I live simultaneously, I am truly and eternally grateful.

*You've got to
get up every morning
with a smile on your face,
and show the world all the
love in your heart.*
– Carole King

How to Have a Grateful Day: The Grateful Dad's Waking Ritual

Whether you pick up and write in your journal in the morning, afternoon, or just before going to bed, try to bring this to mind as soon as you wake up each day:

BE GRATEFUL

I am grateful to awake each day with the awareness of gratitude and possibility. My first thought is "hooray, I'm back," and I reflect for a moment on what I appreciate and what made it possible for me to be here, today.

BE MINDFUL

Next I consider with gratitude what I can do with the day ahead to be good to myself and to make a difference to others. While my head is still on the pillow I remember what matters most to me, and I make a plan to spend most of my day in service to my core values and beliefs.

BE READY

Then, with gratitude that I have a reason to get out of bed each day, I toss off the covers and spring from my bed shouting "YAHOO here I come..."

BE OPEN

Everyone I meet, and every experience I have is a cause to be grateful. Remember, appreciate, give thanks, reflect, and record it in a gratitude journal, every day.

And that's how I get off to a good start and Have a Grateful Day!

My Moment of Gratitude for Gratitude

I am aware and grateful for gratitude...

I am grateful for my ability to recognize and appreciate the many, many things that I have to be grateful for, the aspects of my life — both large and small, grand and minute, major and minor — for which I am so fortunate. I am glad for a daily practice that helps me to note and acknowledge several ways that I feel gratitude every day.

I am grateful for the focus on all that I have to be grateful for, and the daily understanding of my vast good fortune. My gratitude brings clarity to otherwise often-unnoticed aspects of my life and my surroundings, shedding light on the shadowy corners, bringing luster to once dull aspects of my world.

I am grateful that my daily pause for gratitude means I almost always seek out and discover something positive, for there is so much good to celebrate, and the regular reflection on what I am grateful for is most likely to land on something good, something that is working, all the many things that are going right in my world. And even when I might note a negative for which I am grateful, it is with an appreciation for the value and insight that it brings me, thus in effect turning a negative into a positive.

I am grateful for my regular practice of noting gratitude for the expanding point-of-view it provides by offering a new and ever-changing perspective on my life and the world I inhabit. I feel a sense of wonder, encountering a vast, uncharted landscape; a sense of adventure as if I am exploring new galaxies in space, hurtling, spiraling out into unknown territory, fueled by the limitless energy that gratitude supplies.

And I am grateful for my regular recognition of all that I have, the richness of my relationships, the storehouse of good fortune, the wealth of luck and opportunity that abounds in all aspects of my life, that I take the time to note and to celebrate every day.

So, that's my moment of gratitude for gratitude.

Gratitude helps you grow
and expand; gratitude brings joy
and laughter into your life and into
the lives of all those around you.
– Eileen Caddy

My Moment of Gratitude for Five Senses

I am aware and grateful for the five senses I possess and experience…

I am grateful for my sight, the ability to observe and perceive visually, and for my eyes that enable me to see all of the beauty and reality around me. And my gratitude extends to the light of the world — both natural sunlight as well as the light made by other means — that is an essential element of sight. Sight opens up so many opportunities for me to come to know and understand and remember and be active, which is why I am grateful for my sense of sight or vision, and the ability of my eyes to focus and detect images of visible light.

I am grateful for my hearing, or audition, the sense of sound perception, which is all about vibration. I appreciate the sounds of nature, and of music, and the sweet voices of those I love. The ability to hear certain frequencies declines with age, making me all the more grateful for what I am still able to hear. My gratitude for hearing is amplified when I am on the radio, as it is the essential sense that's used by the listener, to enjoy my weekly program, and I am grateful to those who listen, just as I feel gratitude for this the second of my five senses, the ability to hear.

I am grateful for the sense of touch that owes much to my nervous system and every receptor where contact brings awareness. The tactile sense of my wife's face, my son's hair, the handles of my dad's wheelchair, the cool air as I glide down the ski slope, and the heat of a warm fire in the lodge, all remind me of my gratitude for the sense of touch.

I am grateful for the sense of smell, noting that olfactory memory is strong, as specific smells often take me back to long-forgotten places: pipe tobacco transporting me to my childhood visits with my grandfather, Papa Louie, and the sweet rich smell wafting from a fat-bellied pipe clenched between his stained teeth; the smells of favorite foods, and pine sap, and the ocean, all of which bring delight in the moment they reach my nose, to recall with gratitude how much I appreciate and enjoy the sense of smell.

And I am grateful for my fifth and final sense, that of the ability to taste, which combines with the sense of smell to bring out the glory of foods and of beverages, and that helps me to discern and take nourishment, and gain strength and energy. Taste enables our ability to detect the flavor of substances through the taste buds, to distinguish and enjoy sweetness, bitterness, sourness, saltiness and umami, and so with gratitude I acknowledge and appreciate my sense of taste, and all five of my senses.

So, that's my moment of gratitude for my five senses.

*Wake up to find out
that you are the eyes of the world.*
– Robert Hunter

Intention and Vision

What do you hope will come from your regular use of this gratitude journal? What will your life look like when you live in gratitude? What do you want more (and less) of in your life? Where would you like to see yourself in a year? What will you be doing? What hopes and dreams may you be pursuing or realizing after a year of living gratefully?

Before beginning to use this journal, take some time to state your intentions and vision below. This will be a touch-point in your daily recognition and recording of gratitude. If you become discouraged, and find yourself questioning the reason, purpose, or value of keeping a journal, refer back to these notes and recall what motivated you to start your journey with your journal.

What I hope for from using this gratitude journal...

_____

_____

_____

_____

How I picture my life lived in gratitude...

_____

_____

_____

_____

10 Things to Be Grateful For

Look here for ideas if you get stuck:

1. **People** — Someone you've known forever...someone you've just met.

2. **Places** — A special place you go to often, went to once, hope to return to one day.

3. **Things** — It's not tacky to appreciate our possessions.

4. **Gains & Milestones** — When we reach an important place, or make progress.

5. **Last Times & Losses** — The end of an era, a passing.

6. **Everyday & Mundane** — Those little, everyday, unnoticed, unheralded events.

7. **Profound Ideas** — Appreciate those bursts of creativity, revelation and inspiration.

8. **Opportunities** — So many doors open when we notice and note them.

9. **Highlights** — The best thing that happened to me today...

10. **Tomorrow** — Anticipate the future and it will happen much as you wish.

MY JOURNAL OF
GRATITUDE

Name _____

Phone _____

If found, please turn no further and return to owner.

Today is _____ / _____ / _____

What's going on? *(Where I am, what I'm doing, how I feel today.)*

_____

_____

What I am grateful for:

_____

_____

_____

_____

_____

Today is _____ / _____ / _____

What's going on? *(Where I am, what I'm doing, how I feel today.)*

_____

_____

What I am grateful for:

_____

_____

_____

_____

Today is _____ / _____ / _____

What's going on? *(Where I am, what I'm doing, how I feel today.)*

_____

_____

What I am grateful for:

_____

_____

_____

_____

_____

Today is _____ / _____ / _____

What's going on? *(Where I am, what I'm doing, how I feel today.)*

_____

_____

What I am grateful for:

_____

_____

_____

_____

_____

Today is _____ / _____ / _____

What's going on? *(Where I am, what I'm doing, how I feel today.)*

_____

_____

What I am grateful for:

_____

_____

_____

_____

_____

Today is _____ / _____ / _____

What's going on? *(Where I am, what I'm doing, how I feel today.)*

_____

_____

What I am grateful for:

_____

_____

_____

_____

_____

Today is _____ / _____ / _____

Reflections (Make a long list of things you're grateful for, or look back on where you've been and write a summary based on the last several days of living gratefully.)

_____

_____

_____

_____

_____

_____

_____

_____

_____

_____

_____

_____

_____

*Learn to be grateful
like it's your full-time job.*
– Doug Gertner, The Grateful Dad

Today is _____ / _____ / _____

What's going on? *(Where I am, what I'm doing, how I feel today.)*

_____

_____

What I am grateful for:

_____

_____

_____

_____

_____

Today is _____ / _____ / _____

What's going on? *(Where I am, what I'm doing, how I feel today.)*

_____

_____

What I am grateful for:

_____

_____

_____

_____

_____

Today is _____ / _____ / _____

What's going on? *(Where I am, what I'm doing, how I feel today.)*

_____

_____

What I am grateful for:

_____

_____

_____

_____

Today is _____ / _____ / _____

What's going on? *(Where I am, what I'm doing, how I feel today.)*

_____

_____

What I am grateful for:

_____

_____

_____

_____

Today is _____ / _____ / _____

What's going on? *(Where I am, what I'm doing, how I feel today.)*

_____

_____

What I am grateful for:

_____

_____

_____

_____

_____

Today is _____ / _____ / _____

What's going on? *(Where I am, what I'm doing, how I feel today.)*

_____

_____

What I am grateful for:

_____

_____

_____

_____

_____

Today is _____ / _____ / _____

Reflections (Make a long list of things you're grateful for, or look back on where you've been and write a summary based on the last several days of living gratefully.)

_____

_____

_____

_____

_____

_____

_____

_____

_____

_____

_____

_____

_____

_____

A thousand things went right today!
– Ilan Shamir

Today is _____ / _____ / _____

What's going on? *(Where I am, what I'm doing, how I feel today.)*

_____

_____

What I am grateful for:

_____

_____

_____

_____

_____

Today is _____ / _____ / _____

What's going on? *(Where I am, what I'm doing, how I feel today.)*

_____

_____

What I am grateful for:

_____

_____

_____

_____

_____

Today is _____ / _____ / _____

What's going on? *(Where I am, what I'm doing, how I feel today.)*

_____

_____

What I am grateful for:

_____

_____

_____

_____

_____

Today is _____ / _____ / _____

What's going on? *(Where I am, what I'm doing, how I feel today.)*

_____

_____

What I am grateful for:

_____

_____

_____

_____

_____

Today is _____ / _____ / _____

What's going on? *(Where I am, what I'm doing, how I feel today.)*

_____

_____

What I am grateful for:

_____

_____

_____

_____

_____

Today is _____ / _____ / _____

What's going on? *(Where I am, what I'm doing, how I feel today.)*

_____

_____

What I am grateful for:

_____

_____

_____

_____

Today is _____ / _____ / _____

Reflections (Make a long list of things you're grateful for, or look back on where you've been and write a summary based on the last several days of living gratefully.)

_____

_____

_____

_____

_____

_____

_____

_____

_____

_____

_____

_____

_____

Gratitude KILLS!….it kills self-pity,
jealousy, bitterness, and regret.
– Marie Forleo

31

Today is _____ / _____ / _____

What's going on? *(Where I am, what I'm doing, how I feel today.)*

_____

_____

What I am grateful for:

_____

_____

_____

_____

_____

Today is _____ / _____ / _____

What's going on? *(Where I am, what I'm doing, how I feel today.)*

_____

_____

What I am grateful for:

_____

_____

_____

_____

_____

Today is _____ / _____ / _____

What's going on? *(Where I am, what I'm doing, how I feel today.)*

_____

_____

What I am grateful for:

_____

_____

_____

_____

_____

Today is _____ / _____ / _____

What's going on? *(Where I am, what I'm doing, how I feel today.)*

_____

_____

What I am grateful for:

_____

_____

_____

_____

Today is _____ / _____ / _____

What's going on? *(Where I am, what I'm doing, how I feel today.)*

_____

_____

What I am grateful for:

_____

_____

_____

_____

_____

Today is _____ / _____ / _____

What's going on? *(Where I am, what I'm doing, how I feel today.)*

_____

_____

What I am grateful for:

_____

_____

_____

_____

_____

Today is _____ / _____ / _____

Reflections (Make a long list of things you're grateful for, or look back on where you've been and write a summary based on the last several days of living gratefully.)

_____

_____

_____

_____

_____

_____

_____

_____

_____

_____

_____

_____

_____

If the only prayer you ever say in your entire life is 'thank you,' it will be enough.
— Meister Eckhart

Today is _____ / _____ / _____

What's going on? *(Where I am, what I'm doing, how I feel today.)*

_____

_____

What I am grateful for:

_____

_____

_____

_____

_____

Today is _____ / _____ / _____

What's going on? *(Where I am, what I'm doing, how I feel today.)*

_____

_____

What I am grateful for:

_____

_____

_____

_____

_____

Today is _____ / _____ / _____

What's going on? *(Where I am, what I'm doing, how I feel today.)*

_____

_____

What I am grateful for:

_____

_____

_____

_____

_____

Today is _____ / _____ / _____

What's going on? *(Where I am, what I'm doing, how I feel today.)*

_____

_____

What I am grateful for:

_____

_____

_____

_____

_____

Today is _____ / _____ / _____

What's going on? *(Where I am, what I'm doing, how I feel today.)*

_____

_____

What I am grateful for:

_____

_____

_____

_____

_____

Today is _____ / _____ / _____

What's going on? *(Where I am, what I'm doing, how I feel today.)*

_____

_____

What I am grateful for:

_____

_____

_____

_____

_____

Today is _____ / _____ / _____

Reflections (Make a long list of things you're grateful for, or look back on where you've been and write a summary based on the last several days of living gratefully.)

_____

_____

_____

_____

_____

_____

_____

_____

_____

_____

_____

_____

Gratitude is the most passionate
transformative force in the cosmos.
— Sarah Ban Breathnach

Today is _____ / _____ / _____

What's going on? *(Where I am, what I'm doing, how I feel today.)*

_____

_____

What I am grateful for:

_____

_____

_____

_____

Today is _____ / _____ / _____

What's going on? *(Where I am, what I'm doing, how I feel today.)*

_____

_____

What I am grateful for:

_____

_____

_____

_____

Today is _____ / _____ / _____

What's going on? *(Where I am, what I'm doing, how I feel today.)*

_____

_____

What I am grateful for:

_____

_____

_____

_____

_____

Today is _____ / _____ / _____

What's going on? *(Where I am, what I'm doing, how I feel today.)*

_____

_____

What I am grateful for:

_____

_____

_____

_____

_____

Today is _____ / _____ / _____

What's going on? *(Where I am, what I'm doing, how I feel today.)*

_____

_____

What I am grateful for:

_____

_____

_____

_____

_____

Today is _____ / _____ / _____

What's going on? *(Where I am, what I'm doing, how I feel today.)*

_____

_____

What I am grateful for:

_____

_____

_____

_____

_____

Today is _____ / _____ / _____

Reflections (Make a long list of things you're grateful for, or look back on where you've been and write a summary based on the last several days of living gratefully.)

_____

_____

_____

_____

_____

_____

_____

_____

_____

_____

_____

_____

_____

_____

Just to be is holy.
Just to live is a blessing.
— Rabbi Abraham Heschel

Today is _____ / _____ / _____

What's going on? *(Where I am, what I'm doing, how I feel today.)*

_____

_____

What I am grateful for:

_____

_____

_____

_____

_____

Today is _____ / _____ / _____

What's going on? *(Where I am, what I'm doing, how I feel today.)*

_____

_____

What I am grateful for:

_____

_____

_____

_____

_____

Today is _____ / _____ / _____

What's going on? *(Where I am, what I'm doing, how I feel today.)*

_____

_____

What I am grateful for:

_____

_____

_____

_____

_____

Today is _____ / _____ / _____

What's going on? *(Where I am, what I'm doing, how I feel today.)*

_____

_____

What I am grateful for:

_____

_____

_____

_____

_____

Today is _____/_____/_____

What's going on? *(Where I am, what I'm doing, how I feel today.)*

_____

_____

What I am grateful for:

_____

_____

_____

_____

_____

Today is _____/_____/_____

What's going on? *(Where I am, what I'm doing, how I feel today.)*

_____

_____

What I am grateful for:

_____

_____

_____

_____

Today is _____ / _____ / _____

Reflections (Make a long list of things you're grateful for, or look back on where you've been and write a summary based on the last several days of living gratefully.)

_____

_____

_____

_____

_____

_____

_____

_____

_____

_____

_____

_____

_____

Gratitude is the sign of noble souls.
— Aesop (c. 620-560 BCE)

Today is _____ / _____ / _____

What's going on? *(Where I am, what I'm doing, how I feel today.)*

_____

_____

What I am grateful for:

_____

_____

_____

_____

_____

Today is _____ / _____ / _____

What's going on? *(Where I am, what I'm doing, how I feel today.)*

_____

_____

What I am grateful for:

_____

_____

_____

_____

_____

Today is _____ / _____ / _____

What's going on? *(Where I am, what I'm doing, how I feel today.)*

_____

_____

What I am grateful for:

_____

_____

_____

_____

_____

Today is _____ / _____ / _____

What's going on? *(Where I am, what I'm doing, how I feel today.)*

_____

_____

What I am grateful for:

_____

_____

_____

_____

_____

Today is _____ / _____ / _____

What's going on? *(Where I am, what I'm doing, how I feel today.)*

_____

_____

What I am grateful for:

_____

_____

_____

_____

_____

Today is _____ / _____ / _____

What's going on? *(Where I am, what I'm doing, how I feel today.)*

_____

_____

What I am grateful for:

_____

_____

_____

_____

Today is _____ / _____ / _____

Reflections (Make a long list of things you're grateful for, or look back on where you've been and write a summary based on the last several days of living gratefully.)

_____

_____

_____

_____

_____

_____

_____

_____

_____

_____

_____

_____

_____

_____

Be grateful, not hateful.
– Doug Gertner, The Grateful Dad

Today is _____ / _____ / _____

What's going on? *(Where I am, what I'm doing, how I feel today.)*

_____

_____

What I am grateful for:

_____

_____

_____

_____

_____

Today is _____ / _____ / _____

What's going on? *(Where I am, what I'm doing, how I feel today.)*

_____

_____

What I am grateful for:

_____

_____

_____

_____

_____

Today is _____ / _____ / _____

What's going on? *(Where I am, what I'm doing, how I feel today.)*

_____

_____

What I am grateful for:

_____

_____

_____

_____

_____

Today is _____ / _____ / _____

What's going on? *(Where I am, what I'm doing, how I feel today.)*

_____

_____

What I am grateful for:

_____

_____

_____

_____

_____

Today is _____ / _____ / _____

What's going on? *(Where I am, what I'm doing, how I feel today.)*

_____

_____

What I am grateful for:

_____

_____

_____

_____

_____

Today is _____ / _____ / _____

What's going on? *(Where I am, what I'm doing, how I feel today.)*

_____

_____

What I am grateful for:

_____

_____

_____

_____

_____

Today is _____ / _____ / _____

Reflections (Make a long list of things you're grateful for, or look back on where you've been and write a summary based on the last several days of living gratefully.)

_____

_____

_____

_____

_____

_____

_____

_____

_____

_____

_____

_____

_____

_____

Thanksgiving is a verb, not a noun.
— Unknown

Today is _____ / _____ / _____

What's going on? *(Where I am, what I'm doing, how I feel today.)*

_____

_____

What I am grateful for:

_____

_____

_____

_____

_____

Today is _____ / _____ / _____

What's going on? *(Where I am, what I'm doing, how I feel today.)*

_____

_____

What I am grateful for:

_____

_____

_____

_____

_____

Today is _____ / _____ / _____

What's going on? *(Where I am, what I'm doing, how I feel today.)*

_____

_____

What I am grateful for:

_____

_____

_____

_____

_____

Today is _____ / _____ / _____

What's going on? *(Where I am, what I'm doing, how I feel today.)*

_____

_____

What I am grateful for:

_____

_____

_____

_____

_____

Today is _____ / _____ / _____

What's going on? *(Where I am, what I'm doing, how I feel today.)*

_____

_____

What I am grateful for:

_____

_____

_____

_____

_____

Today is _____ / _____ / _____

What's going on? *(Where I am, what I'm doing, how I feel today.)*

_____

_____

What I am grateful for:

_____

_____

_____

_____

_____

Today is _____ / _____ / _____

Reflections (Make a long list of things you're grateful for, or look back on where you've been and write a summary based on the last several days of living gratefully.)

_____

_____

_____

_____

_____

_____

_____

_____

_____

_____

_____

_____

_____

_____

_____

Gratitude is the heart's memory.
— French proverb

Today is _____ / _____ / _____

What's going on? *(Where I am, what I'm doing, how I feel today.)*

_____

_____

What I am grateful for:

_____

_____

_____

_____

_____

Today is _____ / _____ / _____

What's going on? *(Where I am, what I'm doing, how I feel today.)*

_____

_____

What I am grateful for:

_____

_____

_____

_____

Today is _____ / _____ / _____

What's going on? *(Where I am, what I'm doing, how I feel today.)*

_____

_____

What I am grateful for:

_____

_____

_____

_____

_____

Today is _____ / _____ / _____

What's going on? *(Where I am, what I'm doing, how I feel today.)*

_____

_____

What I am grateful for:

_____

_____

_____

_____

_____

Today is _____/_____/_____

What's going on? *(Where I am, what I'm doing, how I feel today.)*

_____

_____

What I am grateful for:

_____

_____

_____

_____

_____

Today is _____/_____/_____

What's going on? *(Where I am, what I'm doing, how I feel today.)*

_____

_____

What I am grateful for:

_____

_____

_____

_____

_____

Today is _____ / _____ / _____

Reflections (Make a long list of things you're grateful for, or look back on where you've been and write a summary based on the last several days of living gratefully.)

_____

_____

_____

_____

_____

_____

_____

_____

_____

_____

_____

_____

_____

*Nothing is more honorable
than a grateful heart.*
– Lucius Annaeus Seneca (c. 4 BCE-65 CE)

Today is _____ / _____ / _____

What's going on? *(Where I am, what I'm doing, how I feel today.)*

_____

_____

What I am grateful for:

_____

_____

_____

_____

_____

Today is _____ / _____ / _____

What's going on? *(Where I am, what I'm doing, how I feel today.)*

_____

_____

What I am grateful for:

_____

_____

_____

_____

Today is _____ / _____ / _____

What's going on? *(Where I am, what I'm doing, how I feel today.)*

_____

_____

What I am grateful for:

_____

_____

_____

_____

_____

Today is _____ / _____ / _____

What's going on? *(Where I am, what I'm doing, how I feel today.)*

_____

_____

What I am grateful for:

_____

_____

_____

_____

_____

Today is _____ / _____ / _____

What's going on? *(Where I am, what I'm doing, how I feel today.)*

_____

_____

What I am grateful for:

_____

_____

_____

_____

_____

Today is _____ / _____ / _____

What's going on? *(Where I am, what I'm doing, how I feel today.)*

_____

_____

What I am grateful for:

_____

_____

_____

_____

_____

Today is _____ / _____ / _____

Reflections (Make a long list of things you're grateful for, or look back on where you've been and write a summary based on the last several days of living gratefully.)

_____

_____

_____

_____

_____

_____

_____

_____

_____

_____

_____

_____

_____

*Gratitude makes sense of our past, brings
peace for today and creates a vision for tomorrow.*
— Melody Beattie

Who is The Grateful Dad?

Doug Gertner is **The Grateful Dad**. Doug Gertner, Ph.D., is an educator, speaker, blogger, broadcaster, and activist whose professional career includes service to higher education, non-profit, small business, corporate, independent, organizational, men's issues, and fatherhood consulting. Doug earned his doctorate from University of Northern Colorado, his masters degree from Teachers College, Columbia University, and his bachelors degree from Kenyon College. He has taught at ten colleges and universities in Colorado and Wyoming, lectured, published, and consulted widely in the area of gender studies.

As the founder and principal of Emu Consulting, Doug delivers training, teambuilding, and facilitation for a list of premiere clients. www.emuconsulting.com

As The Grateful Dad he brings a laid-back, rock-n-roll wisdom to the topic of dads, dudes, and gratitude including his top tips, quick quips, skills, stories, exercises, and activities to reflect on our own lives and bring gratitude to every situation. Doug and his partner Maggie Miller make their home in Denver, Colorado, with their teenage son, Jordan.

Doug hosts The Grateful Dad Radio Hour every Monday at 1:00 p.m. MT on www.MileHiRadio.com.

The Grateful Dad Shop

The Grateful Dad's Journal of Gratitude:
A Daily Place to Celebrate Your Life

When you make it a habit to be grateful, you realize just how much is going right in your life. A daily practice with gratitude brings more good stuff your way every day. *The Grateful Dad's Journal of Gratitude* is A Daily Place to Celebrate Your Life. Get one or more and just go for it. Includes helpful hints, inspiring quotes, and plenty of room to note what you're thankful for and expand on the gifts that you get every day. (72 pages; softcover with spiral binding for easy use with daily entries.)

$12.50 each, postage paid / 2 for $20.00 /5 for $35.00 (includes Shipping & Handling).

The Official Grateful Dad T-Shirt

Are you a grateful dad, or do you know one? The Grateful Dad now has an all-new Official Grateful Dad T-shirt and we want you to be the first guy on your block to wear one, so we'll send you this great new design for just $20.00. Trippy blue text, on a manly black heavy cotton T, this is the perfect gift for every grateful dad you know. Sizes: MED / LG / XL / XXL. $20.00 (includes Shipping & Handling).

The Grateful Dad's Secrets to the First Year of Fatherhood: How to Parent Your Newborn with Passion, Joy & Gratitude

Get the go-to guide with hands-on month-by-month advice, tools, and strategies for every grateful dad. $15.00 (includes Shipping & Handling).

Men's Anthology

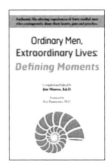

Every man has a story, and now, there's a book that tells those stories. *Ordinary Men, Extraordinary Lives: Defining Moments* tells the first person, authentic, life-altering experiences of 40 soulful men, who courageously share their hearts, guts, and psyches. Doug Gertner, The Grateful Dad, contributed his essay "Full Circle Fatherhood, or How I lost my mother and became The Grateful Dad." Order your copy of *Ordinary Men, Extraordinary Lives* and enjoy the enlightening insights. Gift it to a man or woman who is seeking enrichment, or anyone who appreciates deep sharing and reflection. $15.00 (includes Shipping & Handling).

To order yours, go to The Grateful Dad Shop: www.thegratefuldad.org/shop or use the order form on the next page.

Order Form

Item	Quantity		@ Price	Total Price for This Item
The Grateful Dad's Journal of Gratitude	_____	Each	$12.50	$_____
	_____	Sets of 2	$20	$_____
	_____	Sets of 5	$35	$_____
The Official Grateful Dad T-Shirt	_____	Medium	$20	$_____
	_____	Large	$20	$_____
	_____	X-L	$20	$_____
	_____	2X-L	$20	$_____
The Grateful Dad's Secrets to the First Year of Fatherhood	_____		$15	$_____
The Men's Anthology	_____		$15	$_____
			TOTAL*	$_____

All prices include shipping and handling.

Name _____

Phone _____ Email _____

Shipping address:

Street _____ Apt. No. _____

City _____ State _____ Zip _____

Means of Payment: ❏ Check (Enclosed)   ❏ Credit Card

❏ Visa   ❏ MasterCard   ❏ Other:_____

Card Number _____

Expiration Date _____ Security Code _____

Billing Address (if different from shipping address):

Street _____ Apt. No. _____

City _____ State _____ Zip _____

Mail to: Doug Gertner, Ph.D., 7949 East 28th Place, Denver, CO 80238